Teacher copy

Red Hot

Recorder Tutor 1

Sarah Watts

kevin
mayhew

**kevin
mayhew**

First published in Great Britain in 2004 by Kevin Mayhew Ltd
Buxhall, Stowmarket, Suffolk IP14 3BW
Tel: +44 (0) 1449 737978 Fax: +44 (0) 1449 737834
E-mail: info@kevinmayhewltd.com

www.kevinmayhew.com

ISBN 978 1 84417 861 2
ISMN M 57024 263 4
Catalogue No. 3611785

Cover design: Rob Mortonson
Music setter: Tracy Cook

Printed and bound in Great Britain

Contents

Foreword

In *Red Hot Recorder Tutor* it has been my intention to combine best practice with a fun approach, thereby giving the new player a firm technique on which to develop their skills, while making the actual learning process really enjoyable.

I have included lots of pieces with 'feel good' accompaniments, rhythms to clap to, 'tap dance type' music, optional second and third parts for ensemble work right from the start, 'playing by ear' with a CD backing, and even an accompaniment for long-note practice.

Red Hot Recorder Tutor comes as two books – one for the pupil which includes all the teaching material, and this one for the teacher which has the piano accompaniments.

Red Hot Recorder Tutor is very much in my style of music-making and I will be thrilled if other teachers and their pupils find this book useful and enjoyable.

Sarah Watts

Special Thanks

To Sue Butler and John Everingham for casting a professional eye over this manuscript and lending their technical expertise.

Also many thanks to the following people for technical advice, suggestions and feedback. I hope they enjoy the finished product.

Rachel Gregory	Mandi Meek
Mike Oliver	Jackey Birch
Mary McKinnel	Christine Lawrence
Philip Evry	Len Smith
Tina Gandy	Alison Garbeth
Marie Price	Roger Witney
Rita Porzi	Maggie Holloway
Christine Newman	

Music Set 1

GLORY B!

To introduce B

B B BLUES

A BIT MORE TIME

To introduce ♩ =

Music Set 2

THINKING

To introduce A

WET AND WINDY

To practise the B, A fingering pattern

HOW ABOUT THIS?

by Chloe and Sarah

Practice (♩ = 92)
Performance (♩ = 146)

RAZZA SAZZA

To introduce simple ensemble work

Practice (♩ = 100)
Performance (♩ = 140)

D.S. al Fine

D.S. al Fine

13

Music Set 3

SKAT CAT SWING

For Martha

To introduce G

D.S. al Fine

Red Hot
Recorder Tutor 1

MIKE OLIVER'S TANK TOP

By Sarah and Martha

To introduce quavers and reinforce tonguing technique

Practice (♩=100)
Performance (♩= 160)

CHILLED

For Alexandra Cansdale

To practise playing quavers

Lazily (♩ = 96)

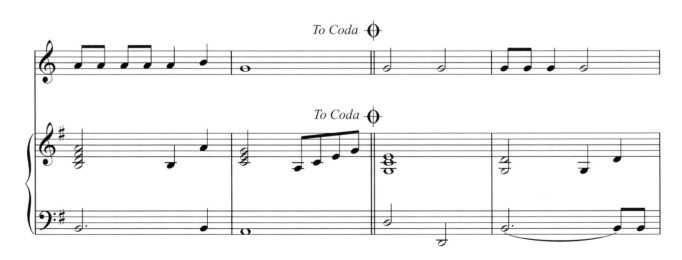

(Student part written out)

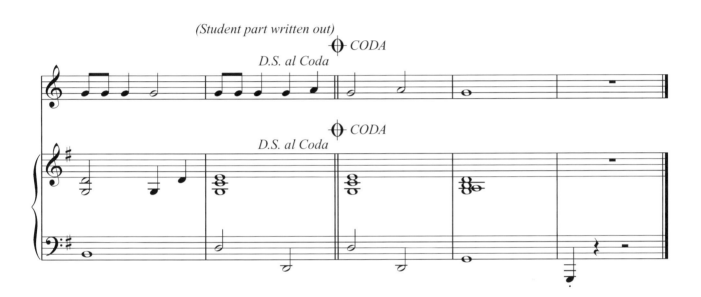

GOBSTOPPER WALTZ

To introduce $\frac{3}{4}$ 𝅗𝅥.

Practice (♩ = 94)
Performance (♩ = 142)

With a lilt

NIGHT LIGHT

To practise the E, G fingering pattern

Gently (♩ = 106)

(recorder part written with repeats)

23

Red
Hot
Recorder Tutor 1

GOT THE E B G B'S!

To practise the E, G, B fingering patterns

Practice ($\quad$ = 82)
Performance ($\quad$ = 125)

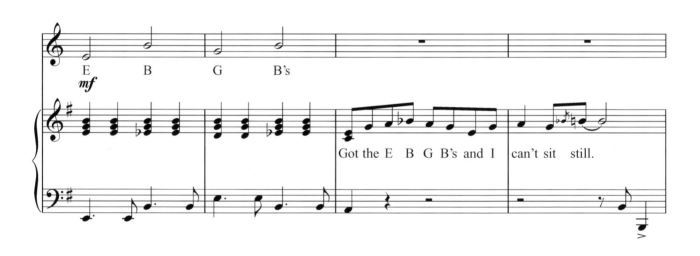

Got the E B G B's and I can't sit still.

E B G B's give me a thrill.

SHRIMPS ON TOUR

Practice ($\quad$ = 74)
Performance ($\quad$ = 118)

Latin feel

Music Set 5

TEA WITH THE TUMBERS

For Sophie and James

To introduce low D

DUBLIN DAN

Practice (♩ = 96)
Performance (♩ = 86)

ST LEWIS BLUES

Practice (♩ = 100)
Performance (♩ = 156)

Red Hot
Recorder Tutor 1

LOTTIE COLLINS' LAMENT

For Granny

To practise the E, F♯ fingering pattern

TOBOGGAN MAN

For Chris

To practise the D, F♯, E fingering patterns

AV'S ANTHEM

For Avril Dankworth

Play 3 times

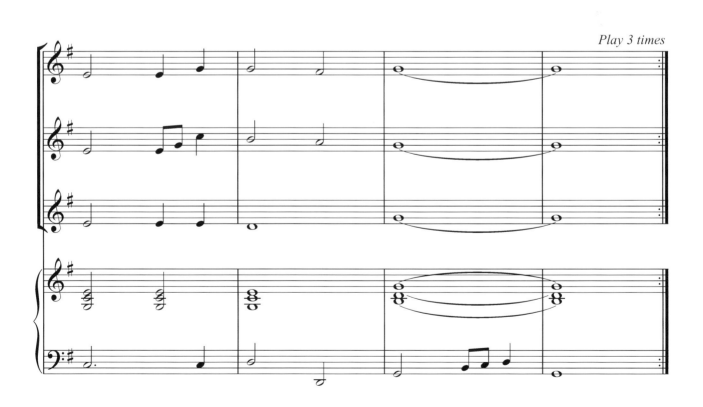

TOTALLY BLESSED

For Sarah Herbert

To practise the A, C fingering pattern

SHRIMP ISLAND

To introduce the slur

Relaxed (♩ = 90)

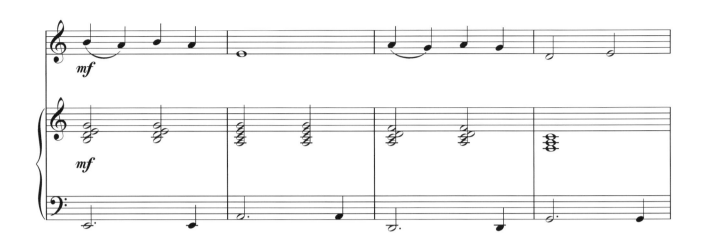

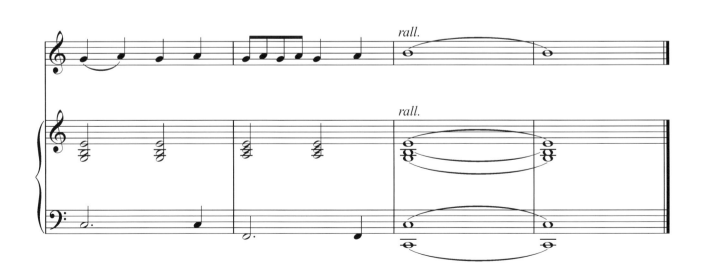

C SIDE ROCK!

For the Wickings

Practice (♩ = 84)
Performance (♩ = 126)

DAISY CHAIN WALK

For Lucy Hibberd

To practise the D, B fingering pattern

THE SLEEPING BAG WALTZ

For the Shrimpettes

A PIECE OF CAKE!

Practice (♩ = 76)
Performance (♩ = 126)

50

I REMEMBER L.R.

To practise the C♯, A, B fingering patterns

DE-SCALEING!

To practise fingering patterns for the D major scale

Practice (♩ = 104)

Performance (♩ = 144)

Latin feel

Music Set 10

SHRIMPS FOREVER!

To practise the F♮, D fingering pattern

Practice (♩ = 70)
Performance (♩ = 120)

MUSIC CAMP VAMP

For Jenny and Bill Seath

Practice (♩ = 66)
Performance (♩ = 108)

2 in a bar feel

DEEP SWING

For Betty Watts

With a swing feel (♩ = 108)

D.S. al Fine

STRAIGHT TO THE POINTE

For Chloe

Play 3 times

Red Hot

Recorder Tutor 1